The Dune

CATHERINE MALASKI

It is June.

The sun is up at
the dune.

We use a kite at
the dune.

The dune is huge!

We can see for
a mile!

We hike at the dune.

Duke can run up
the long dune.

I hop off the dune.

I will rule the dune!

The dune is so
much fun.

Phonics Focus Words: Long u

Duke	huge	rule
dune	June	use

Decodable Words

at	kite	so
can	long	sun
fun	mile	up
hike	much	we
hop	run	will
it	see	

High-Frequency Words

a	I	off
for	is	the